PENNY FOR YOUR
False Prophet

RITTEN & CREATED
BY
TOM HUTCHISON

ART BY
J.B. NETO

COLORS
& LETTERS
BY
OREN KRAMEK

*Check out the First issue of the now classic Penny for Your Soul Volume One.

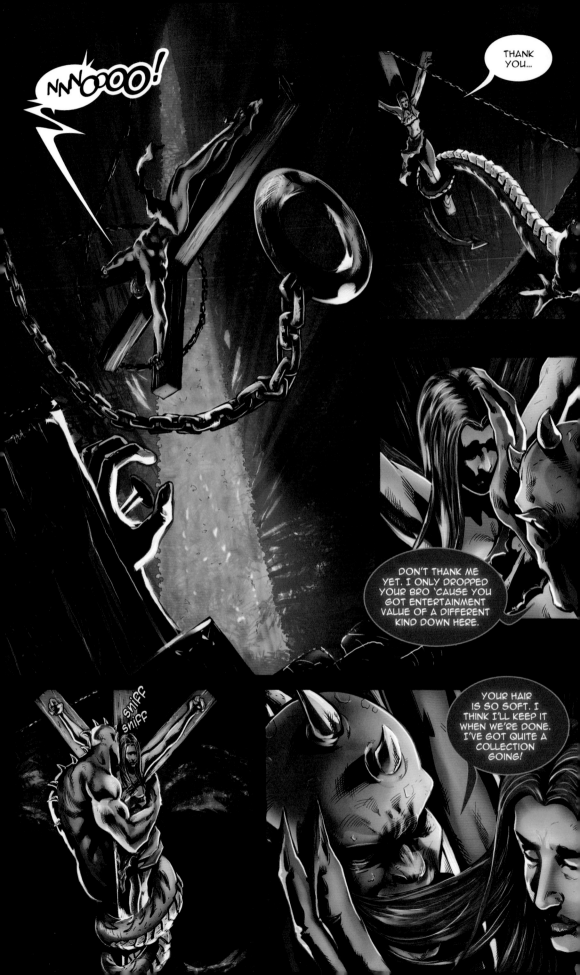

It begins as it ended.

The money flows as fast as the booze.

They get caught up in the lights, distracted by the sex and engulfed by the prospect of winning.

Inhibitions fall aside and man's true nature comes roaring forward.

Desire is man's greatest enemy, and I'm here to feed their need.

It's perfect.

FIX YOUR FACE.

Anywhere else in Las Vegas it would mean nothing.

But here, along with everything I have just told you, we may be trumpeting the arrival of the Whore of Babylon...

Phoebe said we had a movie star who bought the 75th floor penthouse. But she didn't say who he was.

Her name is Alexandra Cuminhand. She is an adult film star.

Not what I expected, but why would a porn star living here be problem for you.

KNOCK
KNOCK

EXCUSE ME?

I'M LOOKING FOR DANICA?

THAT'S ME. WHAT DO YOU WANT?

OH, WELL I CAN COME BACK IF YOU'RE BUSY.

NO, NO. I'M SORRY JUST HAVING A BIT OF A BAD START TO THE DAY.

WHO ARE YOU NOW?

I'M THE TRANSFER FROM THE ETERNITY FRANCE, MA'AM. I'M JOAN.

OH YES, JEZEBEL ASKED FOR YOU.

THAT'S RIGHT.

LET'S GO MEET JEZEBEL AND GET A DRINK. AFTER THE NEWS I JUST GOT, I THINK I'M GONNA NEED TO BLOW OFF SOME STEAM.

TO BE CONTINUED IN
JOAN OF ARC:
FROM THE ASHES

False Prophet

VARIANT COVER GALLERY

ROB DUENAS #1 RETAIL VARIANT

BALTIMORE CMIC CON #1 NATALI SANDERS

ROB DUENAS #2 RETAIL VARIANT

NEW YORK CMIC CON #1 NATALI SANDI

SON COMIC CON #1 IAN SNYDER

ROB DUENAS #3 RETAIL VARIANT

AMAZING ARIZONA COMIC CON #3
JENEVIEVE BROOMALL

ROB DUENAS #4 RETAIL VARIANT

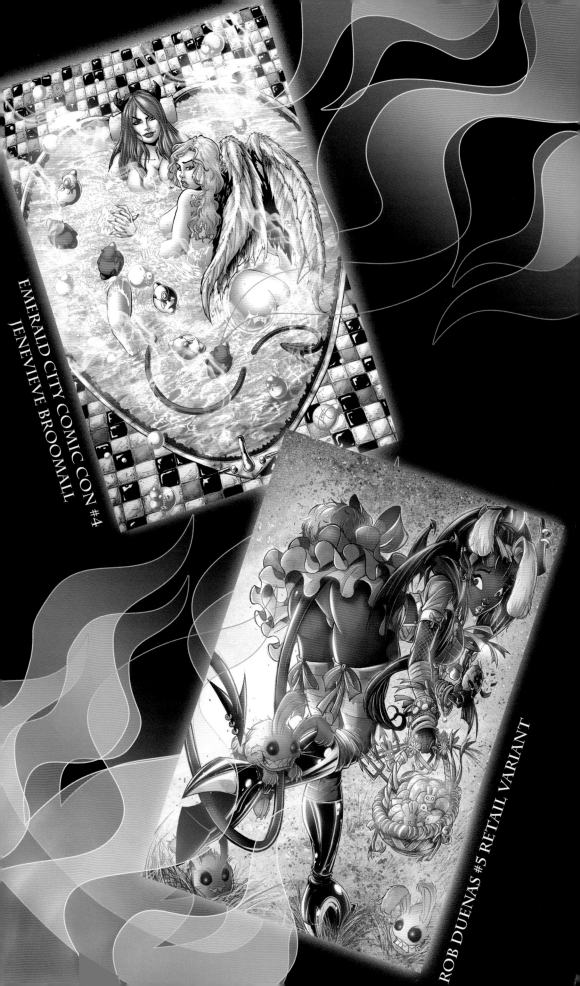

EMERALD CITY COMIC CON #4
JENEVIEVE BROOMALL

ROB DUENAS #5 RETAIL VARIANT

PHOENIX COMIC CON #5 BLOND

PHOENIX COMIC CON #5 BLOND

ROB DUENAS #6 RETAIL VARIANT

ROB DUENAS #7 RETAIL VARIANT

BALTIMORE COMIC CON #7
ALISSON BORGES

CHICAGO COMIC CON #7 NATALI SANDERS